Hooray for Hair!

by Tish Rabe

from a script by Karen Moonah

illustrated by Tom Brannon

BANTAM BOOKS

Hooray for Hair!

HOORAY FOR HAIR
A BANTAM BOOK 978 0 857 51362 5

First published in Great Britain by Bantam,
an imprint of Random House Children's Publishers UK
A Random House Group Company

This edition published 2013

Bantam Books are published by Random House Children's Publishers UK,
61–63 Uxbridge Road, London W5 5SA

www.randomhousechildrens.co.uk
www.randomhouse.co.uk

Addresses for companies within The Random House Group Limited can be found at: www.
randomhouse.co.uk/offices.htm

THE RANDOM HOUSE GROUP Limited Reg. No. 954009

A CIP catalogue record for this book is available from the British Library.

Printed in China

"Crazy Hair Day in school
is tomorrow," said Nick.
"We need crazy hair
and we both need it quick.
Short on the top?
Or long on each side?
Straight, wavy, or curly?
I just can't decide."

"Did you say crazy hair?"
said the Cat. "Jump in back.
Today I will take you
to visit a yak.
His hair is yak-tastic.
It's shaggy and thick."
"Sounds like a really cool
hairstyle," said Nick.

"Welcome to Hilly Hazair,"
said the yak.
"It's been a long time
and I'm glad you are back."

"You have nice hair,

Mister Yak," Sally said.

"I wish I had hair

just like yours on my head."

"Please," said the yak,

"just call me Yancy.

My hair is shaggy,

but not very fancy."

"If it's yak hair you want,"
said the Cat, "I'll show you
just what my new
Wig-o-lator can do!

"It springs and it sings,

and in just a short while,

it will give both of you

a super hairstyle.

"You'll love your new look!"

The Cat lowered the hood.

"Oh boy!" whispered Nick.

"This is gonna be good."

The Cat pushed a button
and the thing started dinging.
Buzzers were buzzing.
Bells began ringing.

"It tickles!" said Nick.

"This is fun!" Sally said.

"It is putting a wig

on the top of my head."

In less than a minute

both Sally and Nick

had hair like a yak's.

It was shaggy and thick.

"You look great!" said Yancy.

"It's easy to see,

with your thick, shaggy hair,

you two look just like me."

"It's cold here in
Hilly Hazair," Sally said.
"The only thing warm
is the top of my head.
It's fun to have thick hair
like Yancy has got,
but in summer this thick hair
would really be hot."

"Then you'd need hair

of a much different sort.

Like my friend," said the Cat,

"who has hair that is short.

"I will take you

to Blue-Puddle-a-Roo

to meet Celia the Seal.

She can't wait to meet you."

"Hey, Cat!" cried Celia.

"I've been waiting all week."

"Celia," said the Cat,

"has short hair that is sleek."

"Jump in, kids," said Celia.

"The water is fine.

If you're a fur seal,

you need short hair like mine."

"The water's so cold,"
said Sally. "How do you
swim all day long
in Blue-Puddle-a-Roo?"

"I've two layers of hair,"
Celia said. "This is why
though the top one gets wet,
my skin still stays dry.

"I just jump in
the water, and poof!
I'm warm because
my hair's waterproof."

Yak

Seal

Porcupine

"On my Wig-o-lator,"
the Cat said, "this wheel
will spin to give you
the hair of a seal!"

"It feels good," said Sally.

"But I just don't know

if yak hair or seal hair

is how we should go.

"Long hair is warmer,

but short hair is neat."

"Come on!" said the Cat.

"There's one more friend to meet.

"Here in Poki Moloki

lives a good friend of mine.

His name is Quincy.

He's a fine porcupine.

Quincy has talent.

He's really the best.

He can fluff up his quills

in a porcupine crest."

"Hello, Cat," said Quincy.

"Be careful. Stand back!

My sharp quills protect me

from any attack.

My quills are like hair,

but they're sharp to the touch.

Do you have quills, Nick?"

Nick said, "No, not so much."

"To the Wig-o-lator!" the Cat cried.

"Don't run! Get in line.

And you'll soon have quills

like a fine porcupine.

This is a hairstyle

that everyone likes.

Soon you will each have . . .

". . . a head full of spikes!"

"We look pretty sharp,"
Sally said with a smile.

"But I'm not sure that
porcupine quills are our style."

"It's time to head back,"
said the Cat. "So let's fly!"
"See you later!" said Quincy.
The kids called, "Goodbye!"

"Cat," Sally said,

"before we went to Hazair,

I'd never seen so many

new kinds of hair.

Hair keeps yaks warm

and keeps a seal dry.

Quills protect Quincy,

who's such a nice guy."

"You're right," said the Cat.
"Hair is not just for show.
It can help you stay warm
in the cold winter snow.
It keeps porcupines
from becoming a meal
and helps keep you dry
if you are a fur seal."

"For Crazy Hair Day," said Nick,
"what we'll do
is have yak hair and seal hair
and porcupine, too!

44

"Crazy Hair Day is
going to be great.
Let's both get up early
so we won't be late."

"How was Crazy Hair Day
today?" asked the Cat.
"I wore," said Nick,
"a yak-seal-porcupine hat.
Having yak-seal-porcupine
hair wasn't bad,
but now I'll go back
to the hair . . .

"How was Crazy Hair Day
today?" asked the Cat.
"I wore," said Nick,
"a yak-seal-porcupine hat.
Having yak-seal-porcupine
hair wasn't bad,
but now I'll go back
to the hair . . .

"Crazy Hair Day is
going to be great.
Let's both get up early
so we won't be late."

"... that I had!"